Claims *to* Fame
Twelve Short Biographies
Book 1

Carol Einstein

EDUCATORS PUBLISHING SERVICE
Cambridge and Toronto

Printed in U.S.A.

ISBN 0-8388-2374-2
978-0-8388-2374-3

4 5 6 7 8 PP 10 09 08 07 06

To my husband, who encouraged and
helped me every step of the way.
With thanks and love,
C.S.E.

Contents

Acknowledgments

To those no longer here: Bernice Einstein, Recha Einstein-Weil, and Julie Weil.

To my colleagues, friends, and family: Joan Amron, Bonnie Tiburzi Caputo, Susanna Einstein, Maureen Farbstein, Bonnie Long, Sara Ogger, Rosalind Smith, and Charles Thompson. You were always willing to listen and to help.

New York City

Dear Reader,

Before you start reading these stories, I want to tell you how I came to write this book. When I was your age, I always loved hearing family stories about the interesting things my grandmother and great aunts did when they were young. I also loved reading stories about real people who had lived before I was born. When I grew up and started working with children, many of my students said they wished there were more books telling about women who had lived long ago. Then my students told me they would like some of the stories to be about men, too, and about people living right now. So in this book you will find all of these kinds of stories.

I hope that you enjoy reading them and find these lives as interesting as I did.

Carol Einstein

Photo by Hans U. Neukomm

Sibbell Ludington
1761–1839

Many people have heard about Paul Revere. During the **American Revolution** this patriot rode his horse through a part of Massachusetts warning people that the British were coming. But most people don't know about sixteen-year-old Sibbell Ludington. On a very dark, rainy night in 1777, she galloped forty miles on New York roads carrying another message to help her country fight the British.

1

Sibbell was born in 1761 in Fredericksburg, New York, the oldest of twelve children. On the night of April 26, 1777, she was putting her younger brothers and sisters to bed, just as a very tired messenger rode up to the Ludington house. Quickly he told her father, who was a colonel in the local **militia,** that the British were burning the nearby town of Danbury, Connecticut. All the guns and supplies for the entire region were stored in Danbury. Colonel Ludington was ordered to gather the 400 men in his **regiment** and go there as fast as he could.

Sibbell's father needed someone to gallop around the countryside calling together the militia men and warning all families that the British were burning Danbury. No man was free to serve as a messenger. Because Sibbell knew where everyone lived, she convinced her father that she could make the ride to deliver the news. In those days a girl did not go riding alone at night. To make people think she was a boy, Sibbell dressed in her father's pants and shirt. After grabbing a stick to make her horse, Star, go faster, she began her long journey.

She spent most of the night covering the forty miles of dark, unmarked roads. Knocking on peoples' doors with her stick, Sibbell shouted her news. "The British are burning Danbury. **Muster** at Ludington's!" Just miles away men were fighting. The 400 men who gathered at the Ludington home after hearing her message arrived too late to save Danbury, but they were just in time to help push the British back to their ships in Long Island Sound.

In 1784, when she was twenty-three, Sibbell married Edward Ogden. They had six children. Years later her children and grandchildren loved hearing her tell the story of this important ride and of the day that George Washington, the first president of the United States, came to her house to thank her for her bravery.

...HELPFUL VOCABULARY...

American Revolution: a war America fought with England in the late 1700s to become free of its rule

militia: volunteer soldiers; also called minutemen because they needed to be ready to fight in a minute

regiment: a military unit, usually commanded by a colonel

muster: to gather

1. When was Sibbell born?

   _____

2. Why do we remember Sibbell Ludington?

   _____

   _____

3. How did Sibbell get ready for her ride?

   _____

   _____

4. Why did Mr. Ludington let Sibbell ride around the countryside at night?

   _____

   _____

5. Why do you think George Washington made a special visit to Sibbell to thank her?

   _____

   _____

6. Can you list some other patriots?

_____

_____

WORKING WITH WORDS

What two new words did you learn from the story?

_____   _____

Try to use one of them in a sentence.

_____

_____

Antonyms are words that are opposite in meaning. *Hot* and *cold* are antonyms. Write antonyms for these words.

oldest _____   father _____

late _____   dark _____

brave _____   faster _____

List as many adjectives (describing words) as you can that might describe Sibbell. Try to think of at least three.

_____

_____

WRITING SKILLS

Sibbell was very eager to help her father. Write and tell about a time you were eager to help someone. Try to write at least three sentences.

_____

_____

_____

_____

In the late 1700s, there were no telephones. Pretend you are Sibbell Ludington and write a letter to a friend telling about your ride. Try to write at least three sentences.

Dear _____

_____

_____

_____

_____

Love,

Sibbell

What do you think a writer needs to do to write a book?

_____

_____

CORBIS/Robert Maass ©

Walter Mosley
1952–

How did Walter Mosley become a mystery writer? Walter was living in New York City and working as a computer programmer. His job was not very interesting to him, so he was spending a lot of time reading books. After finishing a very good **novel** by the African-American writer Alice Walker, he thought, "I could do this."

One day while he was at work, he wrote the sentence: "On hot sticky days in southern Louisiana the fire ants **swarmed**." Walter was pleased with the sentence. He thought writing was interesting and fun. In his free time he continued writing and started taking writing classes. His first book, a short novel, was turned down by fifteen **agents**. But his next book, a mystery called *Devil in a Blue Dress*, was sold quickly and published in 1990. Later it became a well-liked movie.

In 1992, when Bill Clinton was *running* for president, he said that Walter Mosley was his favorite mystery writer. This comment made Walter's books even more popular. So far he has written seven mysteries, all set in Los Angeles, California. In each book, the main character is Easy Rawlins, a likable African-American detective.

Walter was born in Los Angeles in 1952. His mother, who is white, worked as a school secretary, and his father, who was African-American, was a school custodian. When he was young, Walter loved listening to the stories that both sides of his family told.

Many of the characters in his books are based on the people that his father's family talked about. Walter says that the detective in his mysteries, Easy Rawlins, "has some of my father in him, some of other people I knew and heard about, and some of me."

In most mystery books, the main characters are always exactly the same. But what makes Easy Rawlins such a special character is that he gets older and changes from book to book. Some writers might get tired of writing about the same character, but Walter says that is not true for him. "I love writing about Easy. He's always changing his life, ... his friends, and I learn more about writing with each book."

· · · HELPFUL VOCABULARY · · ·

novel: a long story about make-believe people and events

swarmed: met, gathered, or moved in a large group

agents: people who act for some other person or company

THINKING ABOUT WHAT YOU HAVE READ

1. Before he was a writer, what did Walter do?

_____

_____

2. Was it easy for Walter to get his first book published?

_____

_____

3. What is the difference between Easy Rawlins and most other main characters in mystery books?

_____

_____

4. Why do you think Walter's books take place in Los Angeles?

_____

_____

5. Why was Alice Walker's novel important to Walter?

_____

_____

6. How does Walter get the ideas for his characters?

_____

_____

WORKING WITH WORDS

What two new words did you learn from the story?

_____   _____

Try to use one of them in a sentence.

_____

_____

In the story we read that Bill Clinton was *running* for president.
What does *running* mean in the story?

_____

_____

What else can *running* mean?

_____

_____

Some words sound alike, but are spelled differently and have different meanings.

Jack has *one* sister. He *won* the race.

These words are called **homophones**. See if you can fill in the homophone pairs.

write   buy   no   by   right   know

1. Walter wanted to _____ a book.

2. Do you throw a ball with your _____ hand?

3. At first _____ agent would take the book.

4. Do you _____ why?

5. Many people _____ Walter Mosley's books.

6. This book is _____ a famous writer.

Walter thinks that writing is fun. How many adjectives (describing words) can you think of that describe what you think about writing? Try to think of at least two.

_____   _____   _____

Walter says that when he was young, he loved listening to stories his family told. Try to write down a story that someone in your family told. Try to write at least three sentences.

_____

_____

_____

_____

Now give your story a title.

_____

Many people like reading mysteries. Why do you think they enjoy them? Do you like to read mysteries?

_____

_____

_____

_____

What do you think it is like being an artist?

_____

_____

Photo by R. M. N. of E. Dubufe's *Portrait de Rosa Bonheur*

Rosa Bonheur
1822–99

About 150 years ago, many people thought that women should not be artists. They believed that they had other work to do. Yet Rosa Bonheur, a French woman, became very famous for her paintings.

Rosa was born in 1822 in **Bordeaux**, France. Both her mother and father thought art was important. Her father was an art teacher, and her mother was a pianist. When she was little, Rosa loved animals and enjoyed making paper models of them. Her parents let her draw large pictures of animals on the white walls of their apartment.

Rosa did not like school. She wanted to study at an art school, but these schools did not accept women, so her father said that he would teach her in his art **studio**.

Rosa kept a rabbit, a goat, and some birds in the family apartment. Whenever she could, she studied and drew the animals. She decided that she wanted to become an animal painter.

When she was nineteen, one of her animal paintings was chosen for a famous art show. A few years later one of her paintings won a prize. Soon people started buying her work.

In 1851 Rosa wanted to paint a picture of a horse fair. She went to markets where horses were sold to make many drawings. When the painting was finished in 1853, the horses in her painting were nearly as big as real horses! People said they were so real that they could almost hear them moving. Queen Victoria of England asked Rosa to bring the horse painting to England. This painting made her famous and rich.

With the money she earned from her paintings, Rosa bought a large house with lots of land near Paris. Then she bought panthers, lions, and tigers that she kept as pets. She made many paintings of them, too. After she died in 1899, there was a big sale of animal paintings and drawings in her studio. People from many countries came to buy her work.

Bordeaux: a city in the southwest of France

studio: a place where an artist works

THINKING ABOUT WHAT YOU HAVE READ

1. When was Rosa Bonheur born?

   _____

2. How did her family help Rosa become an artist?

   _____

   _____

3. Why do you think Rosa wanted to become an animal painter?

   _____

   _____

4. What do you think people liked about Rosa's paintings?

   _____

   _____

5. If Queen Victoria and Rosa met during Rosa's trip to England, what do you think they talked about?

   _____

   _____

   _____

6. Who are some other famous artists?

_____

_____

How can you find out about them?

_____

_____

WORKING WITH WORDS

You can "paint" a picture using paint or words. Look at the picture of Rosa Bonheur and use words to "paint" a picture of what she looks like.

_____   _____   _____

Now use words and "paint" a picture of what you look like.

_____   _____   _____

What does an artist need? The first one has been done for you.

studio   a place where an artist works

_____   something to paint with

_____   something to draw with

_____   something to paint on

_____   something to put the painting on

How many different kinds of animals can you think of?

pets	farm animals	wild animals
gerbil	hen	deer

WRITING SKILLS

Rosa loved drawing and painting animals. List three things you like to draw.

1. _____

2. _____

3. _____

Why do you like drawing?

_____

Pretend that you visited Rosa at her house. Write a postcard to a friend and tell what you saw. Try to write at least three sentences.

Dear _____ ,

_____

_____

_____

_____

Love,

_____

If you were in charge of an airport, what are some of the jobs you would have to do?

_____

_____

Courtesy of Susan Baer

Susan Baer
1950–

Susan Baer **manages** Newark International Airport in New Jersey. With over thirty million passengers coming through the airport each year, it is one of the busiest airports in the country. Susan says, "What I like best about my job is the fact that I don't know what I'll be doing. But every day there will be something interesting to do." She is the first woman to have this job at Newark International Airport.

Susan and her **staff** make sure that the airport is clean, safe, and without problems. One day, when the lights went out for two hours, she had to tell the workers to go with flashlights and help people off the planes, elevators, and monorail, which goes around the airport. Many people talk to Susan about their airport problems and ask for help. Susan also is busy planning for the future, so that the airport can serve people for many years to come.

Before she was manager of Newark Airport, Susan was the first woman to manage a tunnel or bridge in the New York/New Jersey area. She was in charge of the Lincoln Tunnel, which connects New York and New Jersey. Later, she was the first woman manager of La Guardia Airport, a large airport in New York.

Susan was born in Allentown, Pennsylvania, in 1950. Her mother worked as a **caseworker** for the welfare department, and her father was in charge of a construction team. Susan says that her parents brought her up to believe that she could do anything she wanted to do.

Everything she needed to know about managing she learned from her mother. Susan's mother worked and took care of her family, so Susan always thought she would be able to do the same. Many other women also helped her. "When I went to jobs where I was the first woman in charge, other women working there would say quietly to me, 'Anything I can do, just let me know.' They gave me extra support."

Susan and her husband have a young son, who loves going to "mommy's airport." One day when she is no longer solving problems at an airport, she will try something new. She says that maybe she will teach people at other airports what she has learned or maybe she will try something completely different.

...HELPFUL VOCABULARY...

manage: to be in charge of; to direct

staff: a group of people who work for and assist the person in charge

caseworker: a person whose job is to help people with their problems

THINKING ABOUT WHAT YOU HAVE READ

1. What does Susan Baer do at Newark Airport?

   _____

   _____

2. What does Susan enjoy most about her job?

   _____

   _____

3. In what places was Susan the first woman to have the job?

   _____

   _____

4. How did Susan's parents help her?

   _____

   _____

5. At her different jobs, how did women help Susan?

   _____

   _____

6. If you were at Newark Airport, why might you need Susan
   Baer's help?

   _____

   _____

   _____

   _____

Antonyms are words that are opposite in meaning. *Big* and *little* are antonyms. In each sentence below, fill in the blank with a word that is opposite in meaning to the word in italics. Then write the word in the squares of the grid. The first sentence is done for you.

1.						O	L	D
2.								
3.								
4.								
5.								
6.								
7.								
8.								

1. The airport is brand *new*. The airport is not

   old_____.

2. It is so *clean*. It is not _____.

3. It is *open* twenty-four hours a day. It is never

   _____.

4. Rob is so *happy* that he is going on a trip. But his sister is

   _____ because she cannot go.

5. Robin has a *heavy* bag. It is not _____.

6. It is not a *short* walk to the gate. It is a _____

   walk.

7. Rick does not want to be *last* in line for the plane. He wants

   to be _____.

8. Sara cannot wait for the plane to take *off*. Then she will be

   _____ vacation.

When you ride a monorail around an airport, you see many
things. Try to list five things you would see.

_____   _____   _____

_____   _____   _____

A **homophone** is a word with the same pronunciation as another, but with a different meaning and spelling. For example: *week* and *weak*. Fill in the blanks on the homophone plane with the correct words. One has been done for you.

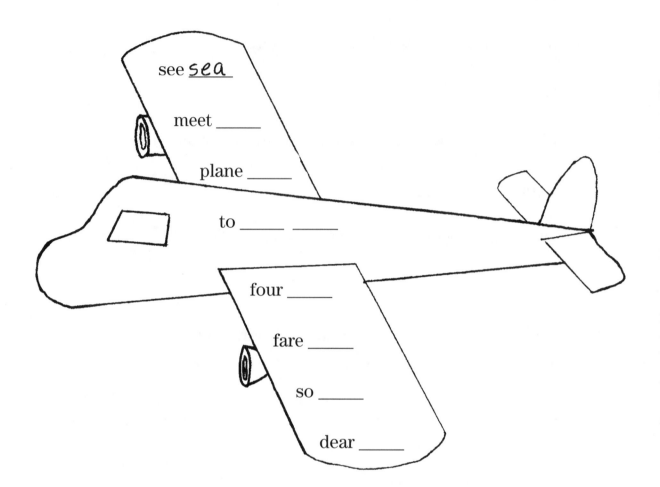

see _sea_

meet _____

plane _____

to _____ _____

four _____

fare _____

so _____

dear _____

WRITING SKILLS

If you could meet Susan Baer, what are three questions you would like to ask her?

1. _____

2. _____

3. _____

List three things you can do while you are at an airport.

1. _____

2. _____

3. _____

Now use your list to complete this story.

    I was very busy while I was waiting for my plane to take

off. _____

_____

_____

_____ Airports can be lots of fun!

Susan Baer says that she learned a lot from her mother. Write about what you have learned from your mother. Try to write at least three sentences.

_____

_____

_____

_____

_____

_____

Courtesy of the La Guardia and Wagner Archives, La Guardia Community College/CUNY

Fiorello La Guardia
1882–1947

Many people think that Fiorello La Guardia was the greatest mayor New York City ever had. He was only five feet two inches tall, but all his life he *fought like a wildcat* to make people's lives better.

Fiorello was born in 1882 in New York City. His father, who was born in Italy, was a **bandmaster** in the army. Mr. La Guardia worked at army posts in the West, and his family went with him. Fiorello grew up on an army post near Prescott, Arizona. As a child, he had strong feelings about what was right and wrong, and he always wanted to express them. When his sister and her friends were playing, he would interrupt them to say, "Now, I am going to speak." Then he would jump onto a chair and start talking about how teachers and parents should act.

When Fiorello grew up, he moved to New York City. He worked during the day and went to law school at night. As a lawyer, he continued to speak out for what he believed was right.

In 1916 he was elected to **Congress**. For ten years Fiorello worked hard trying to get new laws passed that would help children, working people, and older people. These laws were **defeated** while Fiorello was in Congress, but later they were all passed.

In 1934 he became mayor of New York. People had never seen a mayor like Fiorello La Guardia! He worked sixteen hours a day and knew everything about the city. He showed up at car crashes, train wrecks, and fires. He wanted to let people know that he cared about them. A judge said, "It seemed as though the town had been **invaded** by an army of small, **plump** men in big hats; he was everywhere."

Fiorello was the first mayor to ask the president of the United States for money for his city. With the money he received, the city was able to build new bridges, parks, highways, and airports. For the first time, the city built housing for poor people.

Fiorello loved children. Many children wrote to him, and he always wrote back. When the people who deliver newspapers went on **strike**, he started reading the Sunday comic strip on his weekly radio show so that the children would not miss it.

Fiorello La Guardia died in 1947. The people of New York City knew they had lost an exciting leader and a real friend.

...HELPFUL VOCABULARY...

bandmaster: the leader of a musical band

Congress: the Senate and the House of Representatives in Washington, D. C.

defeated: voted against

invaded: entered with force as an enemy; attacked

plump: full and round; nicely fat

strike: stopping work as a protest until certain changes are made

THINKING ABOUT WHAT YOU HAVE READ

1. Where did Fiorello La Guardia grow up?

   _____

2. What was Fiorello like as a child?

   _____

   _____

3. Which people did Fiorello try to help when he was in Congress?

   _____

   _____

4. When did Fiorello become mayor of New York City?

   _____

5. Why did New Yorkers like Mayor La Guardia?

   _____

   _____

6. Fiorello lived in three different cities. Please list them.

   _____   _____   _____

WORKING WITH WORDS

What two new words did you learn from the story?

_____   _____

Try to use one of them in a sentence.

_____

_____

In the story we learn that Fiorello *fought like a wildcat*. What does this mean?

_____

_____

Use *fought like a wildcat* in a sentence.

_____

_____

Try to think of three words you could use instead of *wildcat*.

fought like a _____

fought like a _____

fought like a _____

People live in cities, states, and countries. Each one is different. Try to list three of each. (Do not use New York City.)

cities   _____   _____   _____

states   _____   _____   _____

countries   _____   _____   _____

WRITING SKILLS

When Fiorello La Guardia was young, he would speak out about things that bothered him. What is something that bothers you? Try to write at least three sentences about it.

_____

_____

_____

_____

Children often wrote to Mayor La Guardia. Write a letter to the mayor of your town. But before you write, think about what you want to say.

Dear Mayor _____,

_____

_____

_____

Your friend,

_____

What do you know about a photographer's job?

_____

_____

Courtesy of Schlesinger Library, Radcliffe College

Jessie Tarbox Beals
1870–1942

"Here comes the picture-taking lady," people said as Jessie Tarbox Beals walked down the street. In the late 1800s, very few women were taking pictures. No woman was paid for doing it. Yet in 1900 Jessie became the world's first woman news photographer.

Jessie Tarbox Beals was born in Hamilton, Canada, in 1870. When she was seventeen, she started teaching in Massachusetts. A year later Jessie sold a $1.75 magazine subscription to a neighbor. She got a camera as a prize. She loved using it. Before long she opened a picture studio in her house.

In 1897 she married Alfred Beals. She showed him how to develop her pictures. She wanted a more exciting life, so in 1900 they became **traveling photographers**.

Their first stop was Brattleboro, Vermont. When a newspaper printed her pictures of a fair, Jessie became the first woman news photographer. Two years later a newspaper in Buffalo, New York, hired her. This was the first time a woman worked on a newspaper as a photographer.

Wearing a large hat and a long skirt, Jessie carried her heavy camera and **tripod** everywhere. To get a story, she often had to move fast. Once, when Jessie was called to photograph a big fire in a nearby city, she had just fifteen minutes to get there. Not until she got on the **streetcar** did she have time to put on her shoes and button her clothes.

In 1904 she worked at the World's Fair in St. Louis, Missouri. Jessie tried hard to get good pictures. She sneaked into a balloon in the Balloon Race, even though she had been told that she could not go up because it was not safe. Her pictures from 900 feet up were great.

As she got older, Jessie could not run around anymore taking pictures, so she started taking pictures of gardens. They won many prizes. When she was seventy, she became ill but she still kept working. A few months before she died, Jessie became so weak that she had to stay in bed. Her friends said, however, that she never lost her sense of humor.

...HELPFUL VOCABULARY...

traveling photographers: photographers who work in one place for a short time and then move to another place to work

tripod: a three-legged stand for a camera

streetcar: a large car on tracks that carries people along city streets

THINKING ABOUT WHAT YOU HAVE READ

1. How did Jessie become interested in photography?

2. What did Jessie do before she was a photographer?

3. What do you think would be hard about Jessie's job?

4. Why do you think Jessie liked her job?

5. Jessie took many different kinds of pictures. If she were living today, what do you think she would take pictures of? Tell why you think so.

6. Jessie Tarbox Beals was the first woman to be a news photographer. If you could be the first in something, what would you like to be first in? Why?

_____

_____

WORKING WITH WORDS

What two new words did you learn from the story?

_____   _____

Try to use one of them in a sentence.

_____

_____

Draw a picture of Jessie up in the balloon at the World's Fair.

Make a list of what you think Jessie saw from the balloon.

_____ _____ _____

_____ _____ _____

Jessie traveled in a streetcar and in a balloon. Make a list of other things we travel in.

_____ _____ _____

_____ _____ _____

Synonyms are words that have the same or almost the same meaning. Can you think of a synonym for these words from the story?

exciting life

_____ life

large hat

_____ hat

good pictures

_____ pictures

became *ill*

became _____

46

A storyboard is a set of pictures that tell a story. It is often used to plan a movie. Make a storyboard telling about Jessie's life. In each box draw a picture. Show the different things Jessie did.

Write what is happening in each box.

1. Jessie gets her first camera.

2. _____

3. _____

4. _____

5. _____

What did you find most interesting about Jessie's life?

_____

_____

What do you know about bird-watching?

_____

_____

Roger Tory Peterson
1908–96

Roger Tory Peterson showed millions of people how much fun it is to watch birds. In 1934, when he was just twenty-six years old, his book *A Field Guide to the Birds* was published. Earlier bird guides had too many details, but Roger's book was clear and simple. It pointed out the important parts of a bird, so bird-watchers could quickly know what kind of bird they were looking at.

Many birds look alike, and Roger invented a very easy way to **identify** them. Up to that time, most bird books placed birds on a page by their **species,** even if they looked very different. Roger put birds together that looked alike. To make it even simpler, Roger drew little arrows to point out the important features that a bird-watcher could use to identify a bird. He wisely made his book small enough so that people could fit it into their pocket when they went bird-watching.

At first, Roger's publisher printed only 2,000 copies because he was not sure whether people would be interested in learning about birds. But within a week, the book was sold out. Roger's book, with its simple facts, short, clear descriptions, and wonderful pictures, made it easy for people to learn about birds.

How did Roger first become involved with birds? When he was eleven years old, he joined a bird-watching club at school. For a dime, members got a set of little bird books to study and color. Roger quickly became very interested in birds, and wherever he went, he looked for them. He started making trips around a lake near his hometown of Jamestown, New York, so he could draw and take pictures of birds.

After high school, he studied art in New York City. Then he took a job teaching science and art at a school in Brookline, Massachusetts. In his free time, he continued to identify birds and became a bird expert.

Over the years, millions of copies of *A Field Guide to the Birds* have been sold. Roger also wrote the descriptions and drew the pictures for many other nature guides.

When he died in 1996 at the age of eighty-seven, many people said that Roger's books had shown them how to look at and love nature.

identify: to place, make out, or recognize

species: a group of animals or plants that have many of the same features

THINKING ABOUT WHAT YOU HAVE READ

1. How old was Roger when he first became interested in birds?

   _____

2. What did Roger invent?

   _____

   _____

3. How old is *A Field Guide to the Birds*?

   _____

4. What was the difference between Roger Peterson's bird guide and earlier bird guides?

   _____

   _____

   _____

5. Why do you think Roger liked birds so much?

   _____

   _____

   _____

6. What kind of bird do you sometimes see pictured on the quarter?

_____

Why do you think it is there?

_____

_____

Antonyms are words that are opposite in meaning. *Laugh* and *cry* are antonyms. Write antonyms for the following words:

small   _____

many   _____

before   _____

simple   _____

different   _____

quickly   _____

Write the names of as many different birds as you can.

_____

_____

_____

_____

_____

What does a bird-watcher need? Fill in the words.

_____ book that tells about birds

_____ lets you see birds that are far away

_____ holds everything you carry

_____ protects your head from the sun

_____ a drawing that shows where things are
located

_____ an instrument that shows direction

WRITING SKILLS

List two reasons why people like to go bird-watching.

1. _____

2. _____

Pretend you want to start a bird-watching club in your school. Write a letter to your teacher telling why you want to start the club. Be sure to include two reasons.

Dear _____,

_____

_____

_____

_____

Your student,

_____

Now make a poster telling all about the bird-watching club. First write down three things you want to be sure to put on the poster.

_____   _____   _____

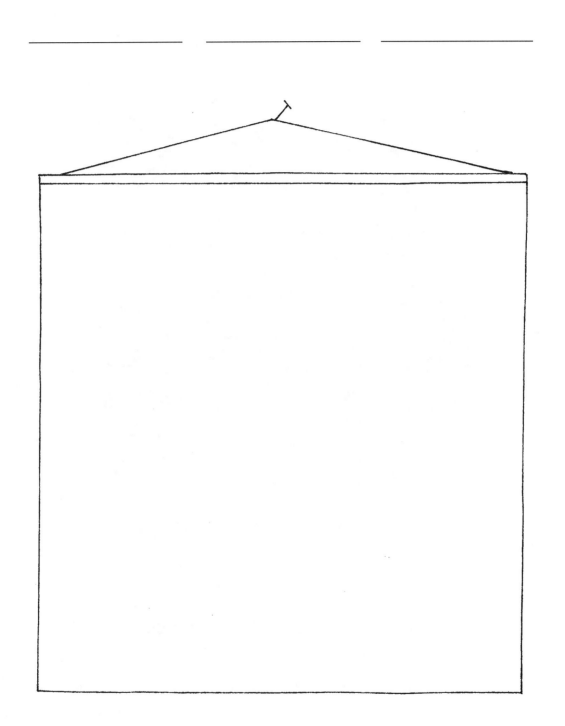

Why do you think a person would want to learn how to fly an airplane?

_____

_____

Courtesy of National Air and Space Museum, Smithsonian Institution, SI Neg. No. 84-14782

Bessie Coleman
1891–1925

People called her "Brave Bessie." She was the first African-American woman pilot in the United States, and "Brave Bessie" had a dream. She wanted to start her own flying school where she could "teach other black women to fly."

In 1891 Bessie was born in a cabin in Texas. She was one of thirteen children. When she was nine, her father left. While Mrs. Coleman worked as a housekeeper to support the family, Bessie looked after her three younger sisters. Whenever a library wagon came through town, Mrs. Coleman would borrow books. Then Bessie read them to the family. Bessie's mother could not read or write, but she wanted her children to "be somebody." Bessie believed she got her strong will from her mother.

After Bessie finished school, she washed and ironed clothes to make money for college. But with the money she earned, she could only go to college for a short time. In 1917, after the United States entered **World War I**, Bessie read several newspaper stories telling how airplanes were fighting in the air. She became interested in flying and wanted to become a pilot. At that time only a few flying schools in the United States took women as students, and no school would *admit* an African-American woman. Bessie used the money she had saved and also some she had borrowed to go to France for training. There she could study without a problem.

When Bessie returned home in 1921, she wanted to open her flying school, but to start it she again needed money. So she did **stunt flying** in air shows. She thrilled the crowds by making loops, spirals, and low dives in the air. Many times she was in danger. In one air show the motor of her one-engine plane died just as she reached the top of a loop. The plane started to dive. Bessie had to turn the dive into a landing. Bringing the plane safely to the ground was not easy because it had no brakes. It just had to roll to a stop. But Bessie did it to the cheers of the crowd. Everyone thought it was part of the show!

In 1925 Bessie showed that she was *brave* on the ground as well as in the air. She was giving an air show in Texas. In those days Texas was **segregated**. But Bessie said that she would not give an air show unless blacks and whites could use the same gate to enter. Because the managers wanted Bessie to fly, they agreed to this.

In the same year she wrote to her sister that she almost had enough money to open her school. A few months later, while on a test flight, Bessie's plane crashed. Both Bessie and her mechanic were killed.

...HELPFUL VOCABULARY...

World War I: a war fought from 1914 to 1918 by many different countries

stunt flying: flying acts that show skill

segregated: the practice of separating people by race

THINKING ABOUT WHAT YOU HAVE READ

1. Where did Bessie learn to fly?

   _____

2. Why was it so hard for Bessie to become a pilot?

   _____

   _____

3. What was Bessie Coleman's dream?

   _____

   _____

4. When she was a child, what was Bessie's life like?

   _____

   _____

5. Today how is flying different from what it was when Bessie was flying?

   _____

   _____

   _____

6. What is one thing Bessie did that you think was very brave?

_____

_____

_____

Write about something that you (or someone you know) did that was brave.

_____

_____

_____

_____

WORKING WITH WORDS

What two new words did you learn from the story?

_____   _____

Try to use one of them in a sentence.

_____

_____

What does *admit* mean in the story?

_____

_____

What else can *admit* mean?

_____

_____

What does *brave* mean?

_____

_____

Try to use *brave* in a sentence.

_____

_____

Write three adjectives (describing words) that tell what Bessie
was like.

_____

_____

What did you find most interesting about Bessie's life?

_____

_____

_____

If you could ask Bessie two questions about her life, what would you ask?

_____

_____

_____

When Bessie died, they found a letter from a twelve-year-old girl in her pocket. The girl had written to Bessie telling her how brave she thought Bessie was. Write a letter to Bessie and be sure to include your questions.

Dear Ms. Coleman,

_____

_____

_____

_____

Your friend,

_____

How do you think baseball umpires learn their job?

_____

_____

Amanda Clement
1888–1971

In 1904 Amanda Clement became the first woman paid to be an **umpire** in a baseball game. Amanda, born in 1888, grew up in Hudson, South Dakota. She played baseball with her brother Hank. If she was not playing, she umpired.

When Amanda was sixteen, her family went to Hawarden, Iowa, to see her brother play baseball. Hank had become a

semipro pitcher for the Renville team. The first game was going to be played by **amateurs**, but the umpire did not show up. So Hank asked if his sister could be the umpire. She did such a good job that the semipro teams said they would pay her to umpire their game. When Amanda umpired the Renville-Hawarden game, she became the first paid woman umpire.

Between 1904 and 1908, Amanda umpired about fifty baseball games a summer. At that time, the umpire stood behind the pitcher, not the catcher, and looked past him to the plate, which was sixty feet away. Amanda was paid from fifteen to twenty-five dollars a game. She used this money to pay for college. At college she ran **track** and played basketball and tennis. But she still worked as an umpire during the baseball season.

Later Amanda taught **physical education**. Then she *ran* a YMCA. She always coached basketball, tennis, and track teams. When her mother became sick, she returned home to Hudson. She still threw a baseball so hard that her nephews put sponges in their gloves to keep their hands from *stinging* when she pitched.

After her mother died, Amanda worked as a **social worker** for twenty-five years. She died at the age of eighty-three. Of all the many wonderful things she did, her work as an umpire pleased her the most.

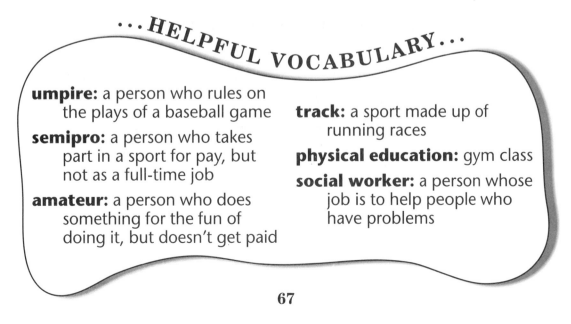

···HELPFUL VOCABULARY···

umpire: a person who rules on the plays of a baseball game

semipro: a person who takes part in a sport for pay, but not as a full-time job

amateur: a person who does something for the fun of doing it, but doesn't get paid

track: a sport made up of running races

physical education: gym class

social worker: a person whose job is to help people who have problems

THINKING ABOUT WHAT YOU HAVE READ

1. When was Amanda born?

   _____

   _____

2. As a child what did Amanda like to do?

   _____

   _____

3. Why do we remember Amanda Clement?

   _____

   _____

4. How was umpiring helpful to Amanda?

   _____

   _____

5. Why was Amanda lucky in Hawarden, Iowa?

   _____

   _____

6. Besides baseball what other sports did Amanda enjoy?

_____

_____

WORKING WITH WORDS

What two new words did you learn from the story?

_____ _____

Try to use one of them in a sentence.

_____

_____

In the story we learn that Amanda Clement *ran* a YMCA. What does *ran* mean in the story?

_____

What else can *ran* mean?

_____

What does *stinging* mean?

_____

Can you think of a word that means the same thing as *stinging?*

_____

List as many adjectives (describing words) as you can think of that might describe Amanda Clement. Try to think of at least three.

_____

_____

Amanda Clement was very good in sports. Write what kinds of things you are good in now.

_____

_____

When you grow up, what would you like to be good in?

_____

_____

Write about a time when you or someone you know did something for the first time.

_____

_____

_____

What kind of music do you like to listen to?

_____

_____

CORBIS/Lynn Goldsmith ©

Ruben Blades
1948–

"What should I be?" thought Ruben Blades. Ruben was born in a poor neighborhood in Panama City, Panama, in 1948. His mother was a singer, and his father was a **conga** player in a band as well as a policeman. Ruben wanted to be a musician, but his father said that he should be a lawyer.

Ruben went to college and studied law. During that time he also wrote music and sang with Latin bands. Ruben was interested in law, but he really loved music, too.

Shortly after he became a lawyer, Ruben went on a trip to New York City. **Salsa** music was just becoming *popular*, and Latin record producers in New York City were **promoting** this kind of dance music. Ruben decided to stay in New York, hoping to become a famous musician.

He started working in the mailroom of Fania, a record company that produced the leading salsa labels. After hearing him play, the people at Fania gave him a contract, and in 1978 Ruben recorded "Siembra," which broke all sales records for salsa.

Soon Ruben was changing the salsa world. Using an electric keyboard, he made a different kind of sound and added other rhythms to salsa's basic beat. Most salsa songs spoke about love, but Ruben wrote and sang about everyday life and things he felt were not right in the world.

In 1984 Ruben became the first salsa star to make English and Spanish albums for the same record company. Since Ruben had English-speaking and Spanish-speaking fans, he made sure that the words of his songs were printed in both English and Spanish.

Even though he was doing very well, Ruben took a year off and went to Harvard University to get another law degree. After *completing* his degree, he started acting. Ruben acted in several major films and on television.

Ruben continued living in the United States. In the early 1990s he thought the government of Panama was not very honest, so in 1994 he ran for president of Panama. He lost the election, but almost one-fourth of the people voted for him.

Ruben has made sixteen albums and has won two **Grammy Awards**. Recently he starred in a Broadway play and a movie.

...HELPFUL VOCABULARY...

conga: a tall drum you play with your hands

salsa: Latin dance music

promoting: trying to advance or sell a product

Grammy Awards: music awards given out each year

THINKING ABOUT WHAT YOU HAVE READ

1. Where was Ruben born?

   _____

2. In college, what two things was Ruben interested in?

   _____

   _____

3. Why did Ruben stay in New York City?

   _____

   _____

4. Why was 1978 an important year for Ruben Blades?

   _____

   _____

5. How was the salsa music of Ruben Blades different from other salsa music?

   _____

   _____

6. Name another famous singer.

   _____

Tell what you know about him or her.

_____

_____

_____

WORKING WITH WORDS

What new words did you learn from the story?

_____   _____

_____   _____

Try to use one of them in a sentence.

_____

_____

What does *popular* mean?

_____

_____

Try to use *popular* in a sentence.

_____

_____

What does *completing* mean?

_____

_____

Try to use *completing* in a sentence.

_____

_____

Antonyms are words that are opposite in meaning. *Good* and *bad* are antonyms. Write antonyms for these words.

poor   _____

loved   _____

stay   _____

add   _____

continued   _____

lost   _____

WRITING SKILLS

Ruben is a salsa singer. Write about the kind of music you like.

_____

_____

Many people like the song "Siembra." Tell what songs you like.
Try to think of two.

_____

_____

List three songs you can sing.

1. _____

2. _____

3. _____

In your own words, write about the life of Ruben Blades. Try to
write about three important times in his life.

_____

_____

_____

_____

What do you think is a good idea for an invention?

_____

_____

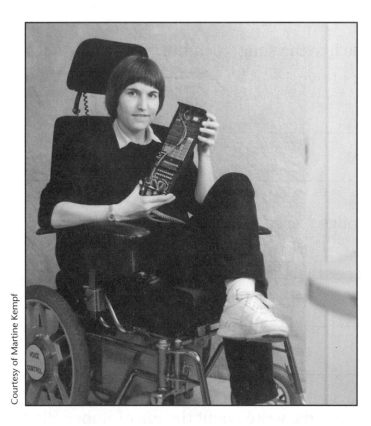

Courtesy of Martine Kempf

Martine Kempf
1958–

Martine Kempf was born in Strasbourg, France, in 1958. When she was growing up, her father was unable to use his legs because of **polio**. He invented a way to drive his car using hand controls. Then he started a company that changes cars so that they can be controlled only by the hands. These are for people who do not have the use of their legs.

When Martine was sixteen years old, she nearly died after eating some unwashed strawberries. She was in and out of the hospital for three years. After this happened Martine thought, "I will not spend my life doing nothing. I want to learn everything I can and do something to help other people."

While Martine was in college, her father told her that people were calling his factory. They asked if he could do anything to help teenagers who were born without arms. They also wanted to be able to drive a car.

He knew that Martine had learned how to use a computer. Her father gave her one of her own and told her that she should try to invent a computer program that would do what a person's voice told it to do. Then people without arms could drive their own car.

Martine learned how to **program** a computer, and in a few months she had a model ready. It was a voice-control box she called the Katalavox.

Martine wanted to learn more about computers, so she started reading magazines and going to computer shows. A year later when she was twenty-four years old, her system was ready. She quit college and started her own company, which makes the Katalavox.

Because of the Katalavox, people who have no arms can use their voice to drive their cars, and people who cannot use their arms or legs can tell their wheelchairs what to do. Martine sells her invention at a price people can afford.

Doctors also find her invention very useful. During operations, by saying simple words, doctors use the Katalavox to move microscopes so that they can see better.

Now Martine lives in Sunnyvale, California. As a child she often played music on the recorder and the piano with her family. Today she still loves playing music. She also enjoys flying a small plane. She is always trying to make her invention better. Martine says that in the future she would like to invent something even better than her voice-control box.

...HELPFUL VOCABULARY...

polio: a disease that can cause loss of movement or feeling

program: to give a machine a set of working instructions

THINKING ABOUT WHAT YOU HAVE READ

1. Where was Martine born?

   _____

2. What does Martine Kempf's father do?

   _____

   _____

3. What happened to Martine Kempf when she was sixteen
   years old?

   _____

   _____

4. Why did Martine start working on her invention?

   _____

   _____

5. What is the Katalavox?

   _____

   _____

   _____

6. Whom does the Katalavox help?

_____

_____

WORKING WITH WORDS

What two new words did you learn from the story?

_____   _____

Try to use one of them in a sentence.

_____

_____

How many useful inventions can you think of? Try to think of three.

_____

_____

_____

Write three adjectives (describing words) that tell what Martine Kempf is like.

_____

_____

_____

Fill the computer screen with "computer" words.

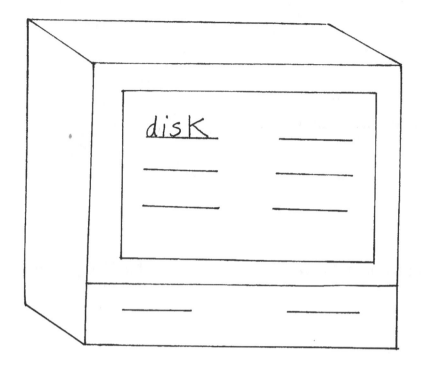

WRITING SKILLS

Martine used a computer to invent the Katalavox. Write about how you use a computer.

_____

_____

_____

What would you like to learn to do on the computer?

_____

_____

Martine's invention, the Katalavox, helps many people. Write about something you would like to invent. Then draw a picture of it.

_____

_____

What musical instruments would you enjoy playing?

_____

_____

Photo by J. Henry Fair

Yo-Yo Ma
1955–

Many people think that Yo-Yo Ma is the *greatest* living
cellist. But Yo-Yo, who is known for his cheerfulness and great
sense of humor, describes himself as "just a performing
musician." His success, he says, is due to the wonderful music
that the **composers** wrote.

Yo-Yo was born in Paris, France, in 1955, the youngest of two children. His father was a violinist and music teacher, who had come from China, and his mother was a singer from Hong Kong. At first, both Yo-Yo and his older sister played the violin. But when he was four years old, he wanted "something different," so he *switched* to playing the **cello** and piano. Since the cello was bigger than he was, Yo-Yo had to sit on a stack of telephone books to play it.

His father taught him only small parts of the music at one time. This way his son could learn it. Yo-Yo says it was not hard work. He practiced only five to ten minutes a day, but during that time he had to pay close attention.

When Yo-Yo was five years old, he gave his first concert, playing both the cello and the piano. A year later his family moved to New York City, where his father taught music. When one of his student's fathers, a great violinist, heard Yo-Yo playing the cello, he was so impressed that he arranged for him to study with a famous and excellent music teacher, Leonard Rose.

In the beginning, Yo-Yo was so shy that he tried to hide behind the cello; he only spoke to his teacher in a whisper. But by the time he was seven, Yo-Yo played on a TV program shown throughout the country.

Yo-Yo finished high school when he was just fifteen years old. Then he went to a famous music school, but left to go to a regular college. Yo-Yo says, "I really wanted to go to college. Since I started very young, I was always in music. And I was interested in learning about all sorts of other things."

Besides taking many kinds of classes, he also gave musical performances once a month. He performed all over the world. Yo-Yo says that he could do both because he did not feel that he had to get high grades or practice for many hours every day. He worked when he needed to. This way he could do many different things. After he finished college, Yo-Yo spent most of his time traveling the world, giving concerts.

In 1977 he married Jill Horner. They have two children. Both his children and his wife play the piano. Yo-Yo is trying to get more people interested in good music; he has even appeared on "Sesame Street." He tries to make every concert he plays special. Yo-Yo hopes that after hearing him play, "people will want to come to concerts."

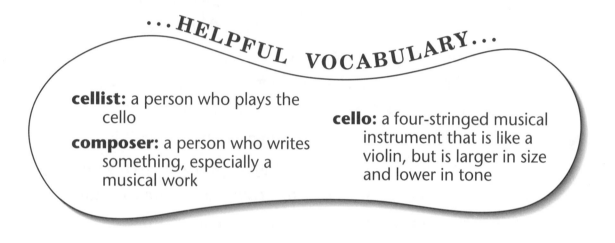

...HELPFUL VOCABULARY...

cellist: a person who plays the cello

composer: a person who writes something, especially a musical work

cello: a four-stringed musical instrument that is like a violin, but is larger in size and lower in tone

THINKING ABOUT WHAT YOU HAVE READ

1. How old was Yo-Yo when he started playing the cello?

   _____

2. Who was Yo-Yo's first music teacher?

   _____

   _____

3. How did Yo-Yo's father teach the cello?

   _____

   _____

4. When Yo-Yo was a child, what was he like?

   _____

   _____

5. What does Yo-Yo think is the reason for his success?

   _____

   _____

6. Now what is Yo-Yo trying to do in music?

   _____

WORKING WITH WORDS

What three new words did you learn in the story?

_____   _____   _____

Try to use two of them in sentences.

_____

_____

Yo-Yo Ma plays the cello and the piano. What are some other instruments people play?

_____   _____

_____   _____

List as many adjectives (describing words) as you can that might describe Yo-Yo. Try to think of at least three.

_____

_____

What does *greatest* mean?

_____

_____

Try to use *greatest* in a sentence.

_____

_____

What does *switched* mean?

_____

Try to use *switched* in a sentence.

_____

_____

WRITING SKILLS

Write about the instrument you play or would like to play.

_____

_____

_____

When Yo-Yo Ma was a child, he was very shy. Write and tell what you are like now. Try to write at least three sentences.

_____

_____

_____

_____

LOOKING BACK

Which person do you think was most interesting?

_____

Why do you think this?

_____

_____

_____

Fifteen years from now, who would you most like to be like?

_____

Tell why you think this.

_____

_____

Now draw a picture of what you think you will be doing in fifteen years.